IS THERE INTELLIGENT LIFE ON EARTH?

A Report to the Congress of Mars

by

ALAN DUNN

TRANSLATED INTO ENGLISH

BY THE AUTHOR

SIMON AND SCHUSTER

NEW YORK

1960

FIRST PRINTING

LIBRARY OF CONGRESS CATALOG CARD NUMBER: 60-6091

MANUFACTURED IN THE UNITED STATES OF AMERICA

PRINTED BY THE MURRAY PRESS, FORGE VILLAGE, MASS.

BOUND BY H. WOLFF, NEW YORK

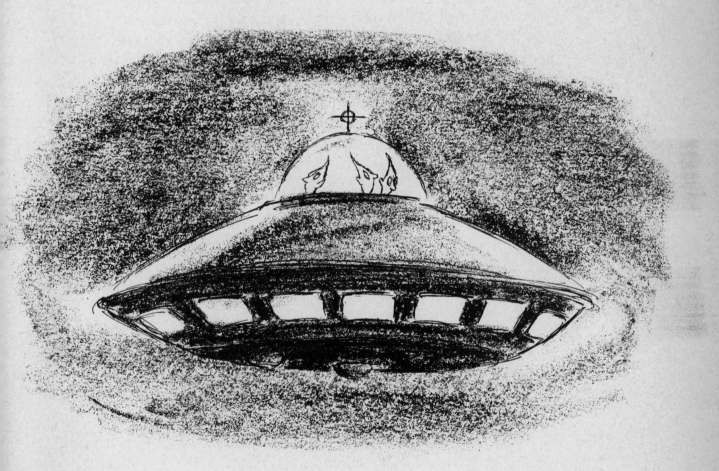

Pursuant to the Act of Congress this 28th day of the Martian year 1,001,960, Senators Koko, Polo and myself, Kolumbo, entered into solar orbit in the interplanetary vehicle, The Beagl, the purpose of this expedition being to ascertain whether certain Unidentified Flying Objects recently claimed as sighted in our skies were imaginary on the part of the observer or possibly represented the existence of intelligent life on one of the inner planets.

Our last voyage to this planet, some decades ago, had revealed such an uninspiring level of evolution among its chief inhabitants, the warring anthropoids, that further contact was deemed unrewarding. Recent events, however— such as the alleged UFOs in solar orbit with an Earthogenic trajectory, as well as some extramartian interference with our communications— make the present fact-finding mission a matter of extreme urgency. We are also faced with the contradiction that the latest spectrographic analysis of the earth's atmosphere reveals a pollution level that makes the existence of life today on that planet a matter of grave doubt.

So, in the true spirit of scientific inquiry, we enter upon the long voyage through space. Although our 1,001,961-model spaceship is capable, with its photon-converter engines, of attaining little short of the speed of light and making the voyage to Earth in a fraction of a Martian day, we nevertheless cultivate restraint, since the slow-down in aging caused by such celerity would seriously disrupt some of our recording instruments calibrated to Martian time.

In the long, nightless days we enjoy floating around speculating on what lies ahead. In the light of our long exploration of the more civilized reaches of our heavens we go unarmed with preconceptions. One is so often ignorant of what might lie in one's own back yard.

Having, as one of the more intelligent planets, been favored over the millennia with occasional visits of the great galactic leviathans on their 150,000 light-year voyages, we are surely more informed than Earthlings of life on the uncountable billions of habitable planets that cluster around the million suns of our own fine galaxy. It is this knowledge of the universe, with its consequent recognition that there *are* other ways of life, that is responsible for our renowned Martian humility and makes disengagement and coexistence possible.

It is a true maxim in cosmic circles that the less-traveled the planetites, the greater the belief that they alone are the only intelligent life in the cosmos.

What could Earthlings know of life beyond their own local terrain? Have they heard of Florus, the garden planet, inhabited only by intelligent vegetation, where the flowers have learned to talk?

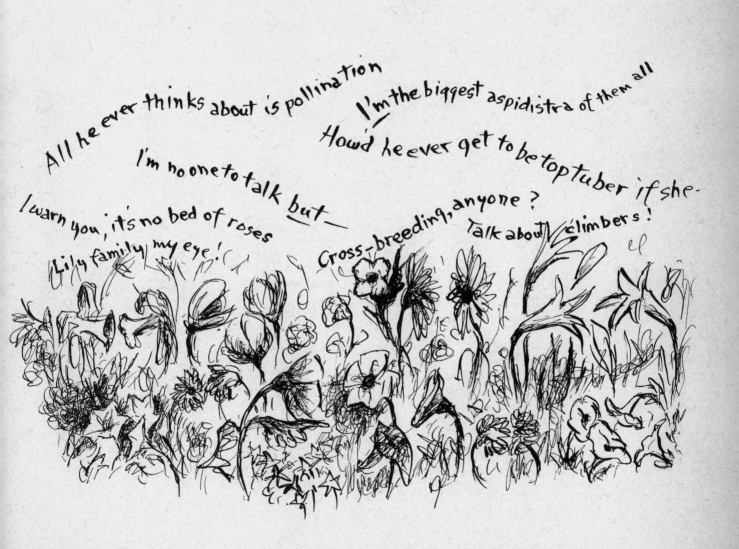

All he ever thinks about is pollination

I'm the biggest aspidistra of them all

How'd he ever get to be top tuber if she-

I'm no one to talk but—

I warn you, it's no bed of roses

Cross-breeding, anyone?

Talk about climbers!

Lily family my eye!

Of Glo, the gossamer, orb of no substance, where wraithlike spirits, pure soul unhampered by body, float eternally through its lacy realm?

Of notorious Fornica, with its exploding population, of hospitable Hi, of Splurj with its unsteady economy, or of Fayth, where they are forever moving mountains?

Of Blotto, where they discovered atomic energy too soon, with its endless wastes of deserted, silent cities, its inhabitants vanished, exiled into outer space in the eternal search for a better world?

And then there are the workhorses of any civilized solar system, the myriad planets and planetoids like Slopp, where we dispose of our radioactive wastes and our garbage.

There are also the edible planets like Fuj, or poor Spud, whose very existence produced the race of roving, predatory planet-eaters, gigantic aerosaurs who leech onto their prey and drain its substance. These, in turn, have caused to breed a species of pseudomorphs— mock planets— that simulate edibility to the aerosaur's eye only to entice and devour him.

The roster is endless. A mere dip into the Planetary Who's Who which every Martian keeps beside his astrophone reveals many notable listings. There's Swish, where they learned to exceed the speed of light only to find that wherever they went they arrived before they started and that they died before they were born.

There is waterless Orji, whose rains and rivers and oceans run alcohol;

unfortunate Stagnus, where there is no death;

Freek, with its uncontrollable mutations;

the vacation planets like Twinkl, where we go for an occasional change of gravity;

Bisol, one of the many planets with two suns, where one must carry two watches and two parasols;

and wee Pea, one of the uncountable minuscules, where life is microscopic but advanced. They have deficit finance.

Many are not round. There are rings and clusters, crystals and ortho-morphs, cones and catenaries and cubes and transparencies

and one— just one— shaped like a star.

Do Earthlings know they live in a universe where only the fittest survive? That there is a heavenly hierarchy, a celestial pecking order with its top brass, its echelons, its organization planets and its pick-and-shovel levels? That in spite of our frequent cultural exchanges we sometimes strain one another's economies?

Do they know that, ever since the war that ended almighty Brink, we have supplanted the ineffectual United Planets with a more vertical organization with the top planet, alone, in any solar system being provided with the cosmic bomb? And that the honored planet in our own system was naturally Mars? *We* have the bomb.

The result has been peace in our space-time.

And so we come, as inevitably one must, to that jewel in Sol's diadem, mighty Mars.

Do Earthlings know that 1,001,959 years ago our Mars was populated by organic beings very similar in size and structure to the creatures we observed on Earth on our last voyage? And that it was a period of scientific curiosity and achievement of sorts? That these pre-Dawn men of Mars had created the hydrogen bomb, the controlled thermonuclear reaction and finally the Infinitron— a computing machine that possessed the power of original thought?

And do they know of that fateful night in the greatest of all our automated production centers, Detroyt, when the Infinitron, guardian of the night, master-control of the factory system with its vast banks of conditioned reflex and memory components that no human brain could equal, became seized with a mechanical brain wave and set the automation complex to work in such a fashion that as dawn broke over the city the production lines were filled with a great marching army of mobile, mechanical and inorganic contrivances, all armed with the power of original thought?

Then the alarm of the human populace, the bombing of the factories, our retreat to the hills. They could destroy our factories, but we couldn't be outthought. How we went underground and toiled through the long days and nights in preparation for the final holocaust— a battle that was brief, for the better mechanism soon won. With our immunity to radiation and our service stations for the wounded and our system of interchangeable parts, organic man was doomed.

By the end of Year One not one human being was left on the planet Mars.

Then the long years of our own great evolution— meccanums, not men— the many millennia to eradicate the faults conditioned in us by that animal, Man; faults such as our fear for survival, which resulted in competitive societies, larger, longer, lower and flashier models with their low turn-in values and a new design each year just to keep the economy going.

Then Planned Obsolescence, a step in the right direction— smaller leg bases, buttons for everything. Finally a button for mutation and the production of experimental numbers until by survival of the fittest we evolved that most viable, most perfect society of them all— Com-mechanism.

Our trouble before was that we had added; now we learned to subtract.

When everyone had buttons for achievement the result was again competitive and little better than Man, but when we limited each mechanism to its appropriate function and place in society—which everyone accepted since they didn't have the wiring to know better—the result was the most harmonious social order known to our solar system.

And here we are, with our great, omnipotent, all-knowing Zu at the top— whom we take this occasion to salute— our unparalleled Congress of Computrons to carry out his divine will, and then the great army of workers, the fortunate producers for this happiest of all economies, workers who are distinguished from us only by the black of their coveralls, workers who make no demands, who are simply stored on shelves when not in use, who ask only oil and an occasional recharging, workers who are contented because, as we so often remind them, *they* own the state.

A planet of Peace, emancipated from death by Planned Obsolescence, that most happy day when we are melted down, metal unto metal, to be reborn again; emancipated from fear, ambition and arrogance; knowing no pain, no fatigue, no hatred; emancipated from the need for nourishment with all its complex waste-disposal problems, and, above all, emancipated from sex with all its commotion. We are truly the happiest of orbs. Soul, the only quality for which there is no button, could hardly interest us less. Our peace is the peace of subtraction, not addition.

But to get back to Earth. The nightless days wore on, and one evening when we were unwinding over our lubrication we became aware of a loss of weightlessness and an ever-increasing acceleration— we were entering the gravitational field of Earth. Switching slowly from solar to gravity engines, we took pleasure in the quicker pickup, the extra zoom, provided by the gravitational pull of Earth's superior mass. It was good to be able to sit down again.

Peering through the astroscope, we studied the surface of the great body we were approaching. We made a sighting on the isthmus between two of their continents and enjoyed a relaxing interlude on seeing what Earthlings can do in the way of a canal.

At 75.8 leags from Earth we decelerated to reduce the possibility of overheating on entering their atmosphere.

At 52.7 leags we encountered a number of unidentified orbiting objects that would ordinarily present a menace to navigation were it not for our quick-acting evasion machinery.

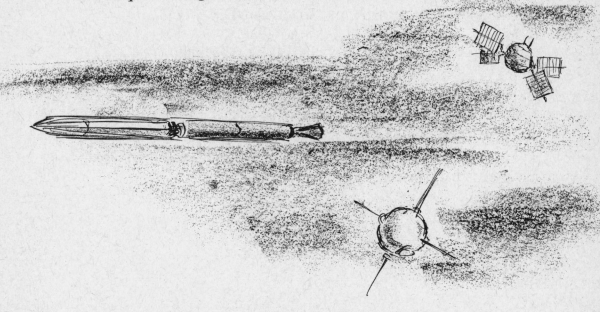

At 8.3 leags we barely missed colliding with an elongated, winged vehicle whose electronic emissions from their own detection apparatus momentarily decalibrated our own. It appeared to be a terrestrial and not interplanetary conveyance, since its engines were of a primitive thrust type— truly a museum piece.

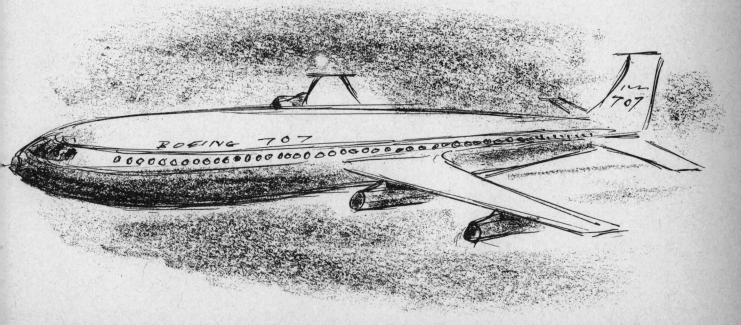

It became obvious that it was time for us to assume invisibility, so we hastened to set our anti-matter apparatus into play. Of course we do not use the true AM effect, since this would only result in our complete annihilation on contact with existing matter, and hence we employ a subtractive phenomenon resulting in our invisibility to the world of matter but not to each other and in our ability to penetrate all matter at will. It also protects our delicate personal machinery from being crushed by the superior gravity of Earth, as well as assisting us in evading the gravitational problems of take-off and landing.

Best of all, it also shields us from their belt of radiation, now becoming more lethal every minute.

At 7.9.5, Mars Time, as the setting sun cast its last rays, we coasted down to a silent, invisible landing on the unknown planet, Earth. Our first question was immediately answered:

There *is* life on Earth.

The question of its intelligence would be the object of our further enlightenment.

First we should define for the sake of the Record what we mean by "intelligence." The Martian concept, which has received galaxy-wide acceptance, is that intelligence represents the ability of an organism, or an inorganism like ourselves, to adjust itself to its environment, for the greatest good to itself and the least harm to others. The level of one's intelligence is evidenced, we find, by the extent of the individual's happiness, by an attitude of love for one's fellows and by the absence of hostility, distress and conflict.

Let us now apply this yardstick to Earthlings.

The leading animals are, as we know from previous expeditions, anthropoids, a refinement of an earlier, out-of-date ape and the direct consequence of the development of the opposing thumb. They are twice Martian stature, with, roughly, two arms, two legs and, so far, one head, all fastened on a single stem. They come in assorted colors and tend to congregate according to hue. Whether they do this for chemical reasons or because the riper, darker specimens do not care to associate with the bleached variety we haven't the foggiest. They are of ample girth and they come in a most extraordinary variety of shapes and sizes.

What we wish to know is whether intelligence is reflected by their attitudes. Our initial survey would seem to reveal little but sorrow and conflict

with but a rare exception.

It is unfortunate that our spaceship did not contain room for a language machine so that we might be apprised at the time of what the natives were saying.

However, we are reporting on our recorders all that we hear for subsequent illumination on our return home.

With the key provided to us by the brief life of a sample Earthling
we abducted on a previous trip— Judge Crater, as he called himself—

To the right you will see Mars,
a small and relatively insignificant
planet in our solar system, with insufficient
oxygen to support any life other than
mosses and algae. The so-called
"canals" are merely a misinterpretation
of the Italian astronomer Schiaparelli's
reference in 1877 to some Martian
features as "canali" ...

the various meanings should then become clear.

How about dropping an H-bomb on Mars?
That will teach Russia!

In order to obtain greater perspective on our field of observations we made a quick survey of the entire globe, the work of but an afternoon, considering the enormous power of our gravity engines.

Politically the world appeared to be divided into two great regions: one, to judge its name from the most prevalent signs, is called Coca-Cola and the other Vodka. The former is blessed with a far greater abundance of consumer goods and is constantly occupied in going places, while the latter, a more dour but better-organized region, is content to sit at home studying mathematics.

The real symbol of intelligent life is, of course, quiet, frictionless government. In pursuit of this study we sought out their control centers. Largest and busiest in the entire world was the megalopolis on the sunrise side of the great continent where we first landed, a city between a river and a strait called, again to judge from the signs, Spearmint. It was obviously the commercial capital of a nation called Radiation Hazard, but that did not necessarily make it the seat of government, so we sought further.

—and all the new buildings? How can City Planning speak of "the growing obsolescence"?

In an equatorial direction from Spearmint there was a lesser nexus filled with much solemn architecture and endless miles of archives. The presence of so much paper revealed that this was indeed the seat of government. Our concern now was to find those infallible signs of intelligent government— optimism,

May I remind the Committee for the Control of Outer Space that we are simply hastening the day when we'll be taking on the planet Mars as underdeveloped—

absence of strife

and efficiency.

It was good to return to Spearmint, where there was no apparent claim to intelligent living. The buildings, like plants in the jungle, pushed upward for light and air at the expense of their neighbors; their transportation was decorative rather than functional; the people tended to collect together in large knots, as if togetherness were an end in itself and the air was a clobber of particles more closely resembling a solid than a gas.

Their architecture was borrowed from the entire world and even, possibly, from one of the minor planets. At a place called 88 ST and 5 AVE was a structure that closely resembled some of the creations on the planet Kokeye. It might even be the Kokeyed Legation and indicate that they had gotten here before us.

I'd hate to live in this neighborhood — we might be expected to conform.

Situated on the embankment of the strait was a large slab, not especially imposing or monumental, compared with the many grander buildings on this island, but possibly of some significance in view of the long row of multicolored banners in front.

Everything all right in the Middle East? Last night I saw a light in Egypt's window —

It could be the city hall, but if so its glass sides gave it a rather transient, impermanent quality, as if whatever it represented was not expected to last.

If Red China gets in there go property values

It should be noted that in basing our definition of intelligence on one's success in adjusting oneself to one's environment we seem to be ignoring the views of Grim, the noted Saturnian teleologist, who rates the organism's intelligence solely on its ability to achieve its purpose. Unhappily, Grim's Hypothesis resulted in endless debate on the meaning and relative value of purpose. Does the state exist for the individual or the individual for the state, and what is the purpose of the whole business anyway? We therefore prefer the official Martian view as asseverated by Whooper, to whom environment includes purpose as one of the normal stresses.

The language barrier makes it somewhat difficult for us to analyze the purpose of motivations of Earthlings, but with our Whooper-rating system we can at least judge whether they are getting anywhere successfully. Some occupations of man, we must admit, reveal neither a purpose nor any particular adjustment to environment.

We are particularly fortunate in the efficacy of our anti-matter apparatus in conferring invisibility and thus are able to carry on the most intimate studies with no fear of being observed. It is true that our presence is occasionally registered on their instruments

and that we are dimly apprehended by their animal house guests

or even more clearly descried by an occasional gifted Earthling

but only once did our invisibility-effect completely fail to function.

Usually we are unseen and undetectable. Thanks to this unearthly property we are able to make close observation of their idea of carrying on the species— a system that impressed us as, chiefly, a lot of hard work.

There are two principal sexes— the male, or drone, the work force of the race,

and the female, or queen, to whose body the male is mysteriously attracted in spite of all her efforts to dress to repel. In addition to bearing the children the queen also maintains the lines of communication.

On Mars we just press a button. On Earth they do it by natural selection.

Eventually a new animal is born

and the race goes on.

In the words of Mars's immortal Dr. Lleud, the father of compu-tranalysis, it's what you *do*, not what *say* you do, that represents truth and hence reality— and there is nothing else but reality, absolutely nothing else in the universe. So, for the sake of our Congressional Record, let us note what Man *does*.

For instance, housing. Of course we Martians know that its primary purpose is shelter and privacy. There should also be variety and the architecture should be gay and interesting, reflecting one's individuality. That would be a functional house and we must acknowledge that Man has a number of such structures,

which he is busily engaged in tearing down

45

in order to replace them with rows of half-finished crates, which he builds and then doesn't live in, for he lives and eats outdoors. He sits around in his underwear; he washes himself publicly in a small body of water that adjoins each box

and, in his one concession to pure ornament, he builds his garages shorter than his cars.

So far the picture is not very encouraging, but we will go on.

An important element of social and economic viability is Transportation, the purpose of which is to get you there

and bring you back.

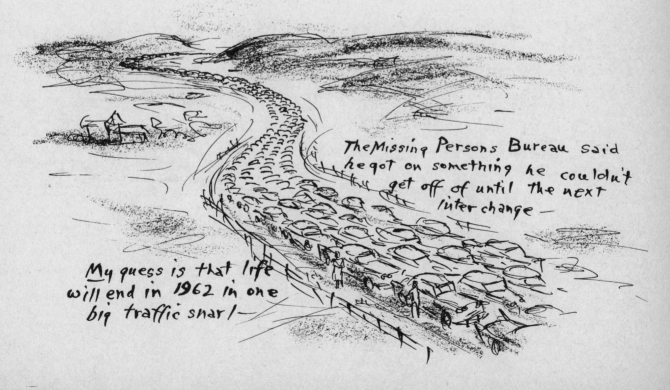

It is well within their technical ability to make vehicles that are easy
to enter or to get out of,

to see from, to maneuver and to park,

but no; they make a game out of it. Transportation is not a means to an end. It is a challenge. If the road isn't complicated enough, they make it so,

and when they finally perfect a safe-and-sane transportation system they make that a challenge too.

So they go by air,

and, in their car-happy, bumper-to-bumper economy, they find a morbid satisfaction in wrecking their old models and then exhibiting them.

Essential to any well-run world is an efficient system of Communication, the purpose of which, as we all know, is to inform and educate the people

and to give and receive the orders necessary to group survival,

thus, in the case of air communication, putting something of a load on an atmosphere

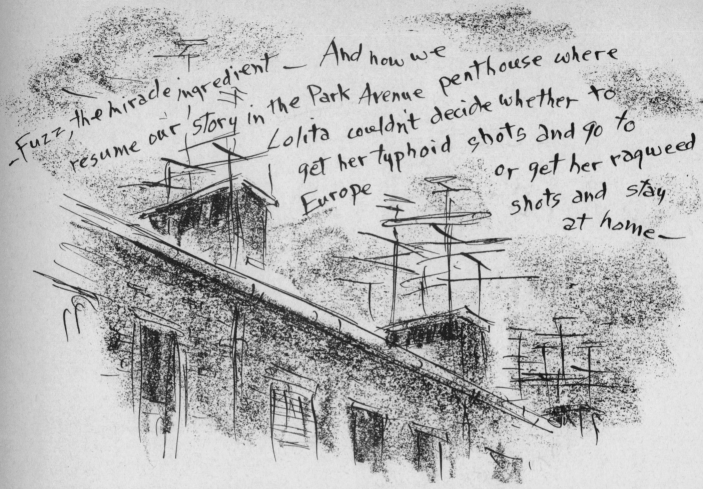

already saddled with radiation, exhaust gases, smoke, dust, fly ash, pollen and smog.

When it comes to Apparel we find that instead of the standardized protectalls that we Martians use to conceal our machinery, the Earthling has created a wondrous diversity of plumage, less for reasons of utility than to attract attention,

since his clothing bears no relation to the climate

and even less to function.

One of many limitations in being a member of the animal kingdom is the problem of deterioration. To arrest the process of decay they have established a system of service stations where, instead of being melted down like civilized machines, they are overhauled, reconditioned and repainted.

In these repair depots sagging muscles are shored, foundations re-built, cracks filled, oil renewed, pores degrimed and coloring matter and lacquer applied, only to add more competition to an already over-crowded field.

Somehow I didn't connect with his world of experience

The right people always start the day with a degreaser

If you smell smoke just holler—

There! A strawberry cream rinse and a throat latch! You were putting too much of a strain on royal jelly.

Decay is abolished; everything continually looks like new. Suppose we raise the hood and look at the engine,

where we find that their vulnerability to the wear and tear requires a
whole army of technicians, all dedicated to the task of Medication

for both body

and mind.

58

Another handicap in the problem of the organic is Nourishment. Whereas *we* are electromechanical, requiring but a daily dollop of celestial oil and an annual recharging, *they* operate on the combustion principle and must continually stoke their furnaces by devouring billions of their unsuspecting animal friends a year.

and by ravaging their gardens, fields and plains of their fruit.

This is a most extraordinary world.

The process of educating the young who will someday run this mad complex requires a fantastic system of Education. Where *our* new production is equipped at the factory with a built-in knowledge kit containing all past information and skills, *theirs* must start from scratch every time a new animal is born and proceed through childhood,

youth

to adulthood.

There appears to be no dividing line between Education and Entertainment, and as for their system of remote visual communication it is in too primeval a state to recognize its intent. Unlike our 3-dimensional, life-size, colored projection that fills the entire end of a room, theirs has a flat, boxed-in quality that makes it hardly worth the effort. Of course we must not forget that *we* have *two* moons to bounce ours off while they have only one.

How, one might ask, do these vertebrates support such an economy? Supply and Demand is obviously not one of their principles.

nor have we any reason to believe that they pay as they go.

Although there is a metal and paper currency in existence they rarely use it; they just flash a card.

Their secret might even be taxes, but then that has already been tried in our galaxy— just once— on the now extinct planet, Pulp.

I came into his life at the wrong time _ he was in the middle of _ long form 1040 _

But in the dark forest of their Economy we come upon a clearing. By reason of the obvious disparity in distribution of goods we can assume they are privy to the Martian system of To Each According to His Needs, since, as we of the elite well know, some people need more than others.

A Vice President of the Teamsters Union, I'd say. A real top banana would have a Ford

Would our quest be more rewarding in the field of their Customs and Habits? Well, their women bind their feet, their hips and their bosoms;

they often wear lenses over their eyes in order to see; others wear black lenses in order *not* to see.

They cut great tornado swaths through their forests

What do we do now? It seems we displaced so many people to build the new road that there's no longer any need for the new road—

STATE HIGHWAY COMM ...

and yet cherish the smallest seedling.

and the pH of the soil is the symbol for the negative logarithm of the reciprocal of the hydrogen-ion concentration in mols per liter...

To add to the air pollution they ignite rolls of paper and decayed plant leaves and draw the gases of combustion deep into their lungs.

They are a race of voyeurs. When not looking at printed matter, at motion pictures, at the opposite sex or at the scenery, they will look out into the dark at nothing in particular.

They are continually going places, even when at home;

they keep moving their dirt
from one dwelling to another;

they worship idols;

Another feature, sir—
it has no moving parts
to get out of order

MARS
GOD OF WAR

And their only real happiness seems to come at the end of the day, when they gather for what *we* call lubrication but *they* probably call nourishment.

The picture grows darker.

It is clear why they are such a warlike people. In fact they have organized hostility into a rather exact science, and states of armed tension were observed that at any moment could break into open warfare.

Don't they know of the Second Law of our great eighteenth-millennia scientist, Phig (who preceded Earth's Newton), who said that for every action there is an equal and opposite reaction?

And how Dr. Lleud discovered that everything you suppress, or control by force, will reappear in another direction and in an uglier form?

And that the great Combined Law proved that every frustration bred an equal aggression and that every aggression bred further frustration and so on ad infinitum?

And that the inevitable result is continuous conflict?

And that the only way to stop anything is to just plain stop and not ask the other fellow to do it first?

Why do they go on? Of course, as we Lleudians know, everything one does enough of eventually generates its own interest and one then begins to believe in it.

Do these organics not see that each individual is but a cell in a larger organism, that one is impelled, as is each cell in one's body, by a still higher organization to carry out its unknown-to-you wish? You may invent your own reasons for why you did it, but only the greater body knows the real reason.

That otherwise you become the cancer cell— off on its own fatal destiny?

But what interests us the most and is the major reason for our expedition is the state of their Science and Technology.

Earthlings are engaged in a great process of demolition, whereby, with each island blown away, with each gaping hole torn in the earth's surface, they learn something. It is subtraction, so you might therefore say that they are on the right track. It is also addition.

All roads seem to lead to a cape far down on the sunrise coast,

the launching site for a missile system of either offense or defense, we do not know which, since the nose cones are stuffed with apes, rodents and yeast cakes.

If the intent is to populate the moon it is not matched by achievement, since they are using an antediluvian method of thrust propulsion that can hardly supply the necessary power in relation to the weight of the fuel to be practicable. Instead of the gentle take-off of our anti-gravity engines there is an enormous burst of flame and smoke, the craft then wobbles up a few miles and explodes in mid-air.

How could these be the creatures that sent those Unidentified Flying Objects into solar orbit so close to Mars?

They possess a primitive form of automation— far from total. The human element is still too much in evidence and there is insufficient supervisory control over the automation by electronic devices.

And speaking of computers, we were impressed for the first time on our entire voyage by the sight of their most advanced machine— an instrument not unlike our early Infinitron

which might conceivably be capable of original thought.

But there was too much of it.

Additive-happy Earthlings do not seem to understand that thought by itself is purely the mind's attempt to achieve security and that to amplify the faculty is also to amplify its limitations. For, based on the Known as it has to be, thought can hardly apprehend the Unknown, wherein lies originality.

The machine was little more than a nice try. Perhaps some day they will learn to subtract some of the conceptual mechanisms and then really tap the intuitive process we know as original thought.

In the meantime we can shrug off Earth. The missile gap— one million years— is too great for us to worry our apparatus about.

We have nothing to fear; their technological intelligence is not far from the primordial ooze. With us it would be a matter of minutes to send one cosmic bomb winging its silent way to Earth with its charge of total annihilation.

It is truly fortunate that Mars is the Planet of Peace.

Our mission, we feel, is accomplished. There is life but not intelligence on Earth. One more operation and we could pack up and say goodbye to Coca-Cola for good.

This final operation is the result of the observation on our dials of the minute presence of the gravi-ray, a ray common on Mars but so far not encountered in our mundane peregrinations. By orientation we fixed its origin somewhere deep in the mountain ranges toward the sunset side of the continent.

It was the late afternoon of an unusually beautiful day, and, en route to our mountain destination, we had stopped off at one of this world's beverage rooms to take a few final notes on their refueling process.

Koko seemed not to hear as we discussed the last of our planned surveys— Operation Finis. His eyes were fixed on the individuals gathered at the counter downing the mysterious elixir that provided them with their highest moments of happiness. He slowly turned back to us.

"I think we are missing the main point of our investigation." The probing, scientific mind was speaking.

"In our zeal for pure observation, in our objective approach to intelligent life, in the very detachment provided by our anti-matter state we have merely succeeded in shielding ourselves from the actual experiencing of reality— as Earthlings know reality."

Koko had a point. Dr. Lleud himself had said that the objective and subjective experiences are totally different things and the latter— the *living* of life— is the real key to understanding, to integration and to sanity.

"Now Polo, Kolumbo, listen to me; we are going to plug the gap in our knowledge. In the interest of science I am going to revert briefly to the world of matter, short enough to avoid the damaging pull of Earthian gravity but long enough to absorb one of those heady libations they call 'Twenty-to-one-and-no-lemon-peel.' Then I will immediately return to anti-matter and invisibility."

It was no sooner said than done. Before we could dissuade him he was on the counter, had snatched a drink and gulped it

and in a matter of seconds he was back in our invisible world.

The chemical was something our alien mechanism wasn't inured to, so we carried Koko to The Beagl and swiftly ascended beyond the atmosphere in the hopes that a change of pressure might restore his mechanical integrity. It was with considerable relief that we finally heard his gears mesh and verbalization restored.

But it was not the coldly scientific, emotionless Koko we had known before. Something had been added.

This didn't sound like one of the proper Martians, a distinguished senator from a planet where aggression is as non-usage as it can be. In fact the situation recalled to us the old interplanetary legend about an inquisitive mortal named Eve, who, having savored of the forbidden fruit, set in motion a most hapless train of consequences. Perhaps Science might have been better served if Koko had not taken that drink.

I sing to you of Mars and the ultimate society — of better worlds — new galaxies to conquer! — Heed me — or I shall blast the living biota off the face of your planet! Who isn't for me is against me!

In some alarm we slipped off his protectalls and gave him a check-up. On analysis the liquid he had ingested turned out to be ethyl alcohol, known to us as a powerful solvent, the effect of which on a well-oiled meccanum could spell disaster. So we quickly drained him, gave him a thorough lubrication and plugged him in on the recharger.

Slowly his speech became more rational.

It was good to hear old Koke's voice in normal range again, even though there was an ominous tone to it.

"Dear Earthlings, you are living in error and I have come as your messiah. Do Martians keep patching up the old and the obsolete? No! We burn it down and begin with the new; the remedy must be drastic. Polo, Kolumbo— hearken unto me. Do you remember that fully automated factory we saw in the vehicle-making city by the big lake?

"And do you remember that computer with the potentiality of original thought?

"And how all it needed was a little subtraction?"

We understood.

The idea was horrible yet inevitable. We would merely be hastening the day of their liberation. A minor adjustment on their computer and lo, the Infinitron! Attach it to their super-automated factory system and lo again, the birth of the meccanum and the consequent end of organic man! The war would be brief; we would vote foreign aid, send supplies, cosmic bombs, spare parts, assorted limbs and heads. And little books of instructions. We would carry out our project this very night, when the automated factory was unguarded.

In the meantime, before Man became history, there was Operation Finis to complete— to track down the origin of the gravi-ray.

It was truly a beautiful planet.

Led by our detection apparatus, we had descended in a wild mountain fastness where the afterglow barely penetrated the compounding density as our path led deeper into its dark beauty. The stillness was broken only by the accelerating thump of our gravimeter as we came out upon a rough road hewn from the forest.

There was now no mistaking our destination as we were confronted by the hidden but well-guarded entrance to a great tunnel, where, in our matterless state, we sped silently and invisibly past the sentinels, through the portals and deep into the cavern.

Finally, in a great vaulted hall deep in the heart of the mountain, we came upon an enormous accelerator resembling, to our surprise, one of our early Gravitrons— our first attempt to use gravity power to create anti-matter on an area scale.

On any other planet but Earth we would have advanced with caution. The only possible threat to us in our anti-matter state would be contact with a negative field of the same state— but this was an achievement that all our observations to date have shown to be completely beyond the intelligence of Man.

So, a few notes here, a final task in the dark of the night and living man awakens to his annihilation and the dawn of the New Order.

For that thing men call Life is only a chemical— Element 150 on the atomic scale— an element observable on Earth only in its combinations. At absolute zero it is a solid, dotting outer space with its fine crystalline dust. Its liquid state is but a fraction of a degree higher, and then it becomes a gas— a gas that combines with other elements to form virus, microbe, plant or animal. Its only characteristic is to make the compounds which it forms grow, reproduce and die.

Each minute uncountable billions of lives are seemingly extinguished throughout this world— lives of protoplast— of insect, bird or animal, yet Element 150, which is all you have of Being, is inextinguishable and merely resumes its uncompounded gaseous state, freed to unite anew with other elements and form— who knows?— a bacillus, a goldfish, an anemône on an early-spring morning or, perhaps, an oriole and expand in song.

And then there are its two mysterious isotopes, L-385 and L-394, the former the light, benign isotope and the latter the heavy or evil form of life. They are found only in combination with pure life— L-390— and never alone, and their presence results in Man's unending conflict between good and evil and the organism's constant struggle to achieve a single, integrated path through life.

Although we have heard rumor of the separation and isolation of these isotopes in distant extragalactic spaces, we cannot accept these Heavens and Hells as anything more than fantasy. Martians know only reality.

Therefore, knowing all there is to know, and with a great feeling of elation, not unmixed with a pardonable exaltation, our mission all but accomplished, Koko, Polo and I, Kolumbo, strode with a proud, firm step into the yawning chamber.

"There seems to be a new particle in there that I don't understand,
but the hell with it— go ahead— we may learn something. Contact!"

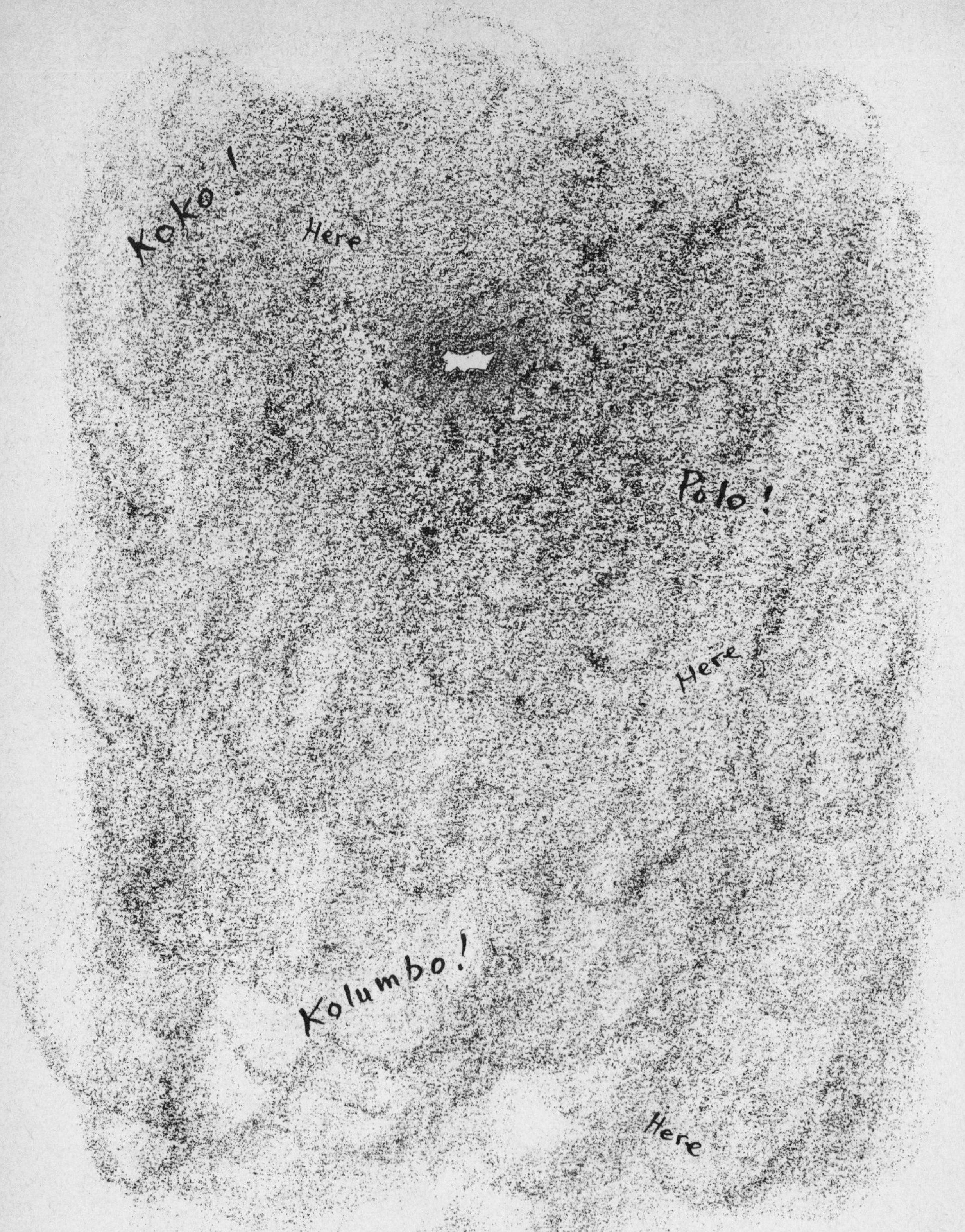
Koko!
Here
Polo!
Here
Kolumbo!
Here

I see a light ahead— Keep going

Do you know, I think we're dead —

Worse yet— I think we've come alive!

You mean we're people?

This is a bit off the beaten — Extragalactic maybe —

Something was added to us in that Gravitron —

Oh dear, I'm beginning to feel things — If it isn't the heat it may be the humidity —

All I can say is, life is hell!

"Gentlemen of Mars, I've been looking forward to this for over a million years! At last you have come to your final meeting place— the point of no return.

"So you thought you could escape your destiny through Science. Well, you knew all the answers but one.

"Extra-galactic, my eye! Of course there's a Heaven and a Hell and they are your isotopic twins and an integral part of your living being. In the heat of fission on the planet Earth where you did not belong, you picked up the element Life, with all its pain and joy— a Heaven if you live it with unquestioning faith and a Hell if you don't.

"You now have imagination. Perhaps I don't exist apart from it and you have created me. Reality or fancy, it's all the same, and here I am to warn you all too late that the Kingdom of Hell is *within* you. You have created it; now you will live it. So be off, my smart, meddlesome friends. To the ovens with you!"

"Six weeks to rebuild the damn thing and here we go, off on that anti-matter, anti-gravity dream again. How do you know there won't be another burn-out?"

—nine—

"*That time something was added—a ray from outer space—who knows? This time, remember, we've subtracted the Z constant to allow for the wandering particle.*"

"I don't like this subtraction idea— there's no experience behind it."

"Nothing is gained without risk, you know. Ready on Six?"

"*Ready on Six. I'm afraid Science is today's religion. Like alcohol, it's just another way to avoid reality.*"

"Everything we ever do is reality— including the effort to escape it.
Are you watching Four?"

— four —

"*I still won't be surprised if some day in one of our experiments an uncontrolled anti-matter chain reaction sets in and we all simply disappear, suddenly, quietly, painlessly and forever.*"

"Be a good joke on us if it did. Keeping your eye on those dials, Peter?"

"I've thought about all this a long time, Paul, and frankly I think the intelligent thing to do is to leave well enough alone."

"Well said, Peter— an intelligent statement. But what if there's something greater than intelligence? What if the ultimate answer is faith— an unquestioning faith in man's unknown

— zero

destiny?"

ABOUT THE AUTHOR

Is There Intelligent Life on Earth? is Mr. Dunn's second venture into an art form virtually invented by himself— the story told in cartoons and text so interwoven that one would be quite lost without the other. His first venture of the sort was *East of Fifth* (1948), a satirical tragedy like the present book but concentrated on a single New York City apartment house instead of the whole universe.

Mr. Dunn is the most prolific of the artists regularly contributing to *The New Yorker* Magazine, and also— in all probability— the most genuine New Yorker. He has lived in New York all the fifty-nine years of his life excepting the year and a half spent studying art in the American Academy in Rome. His formal New York education was conducted at the Barnard School for Boys, Columbia University, and the National Academy of Design, and his informal education has been conducted by the editors of *The New Yorker*, to whom he has sold some 1,500 cartoons in a period of about thirty-five years.

Mrs. Alan Dunn is Mary Petty, also a *New Yorker* cartoonist, and the two artists make their home, of course, in New York.

Besides the two tales in cartoon and text, Simon and Schuster has been proud to publish two collections of Mr. Dunn's cartoons— *Who's Paying for This Cab?* (1945) and *Should It Gurgle?* (1956).